CONTENTS

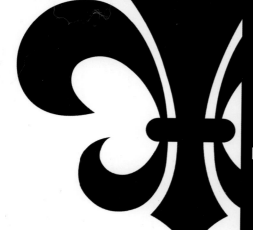

Overview of Hurricane Katrina

Hurricane Katrina was one of the strongest storms to impact the coast of the United States during the last 100 years. With sustained winds during landfall of 140 mph (a strong category 4 hurricane on the Saffir-Simpson scale) and minimum central pressure the third lowest on record at landfall (920 mb), Katrina caused widespread devastation along the central Gulf Coast states of the US. Cities such as New Orleans, LA, Mobile, AL, and Gulfport, MS bore the brunt of Katrina's force and will need weeks and months of recovery efforts to restore normality. Other storms have had stronger sustained winds when they made landfall including the following:

The Labor Day Hurricane, Florida Keys, September 2, 1935, Category 5, 892 mb, Approaching 200 mph, Hurricane Camille, Mississippi, August 17, 1969, Category 5, 909 mb, Approaching 190 mph, Hurricane Andrew, Southeast Florida, August 24, 1992, Category 5, 922 mb, 165 mph, Hurricane Charley, Punta Gorda, Florida, August 13, 2004, Category 4, 941 mb, 150 mph.

The most deadly hurricane to strike the U.S. made landfall in Galveston, Texas on September 8, 1900. This was also the greatest natural disaster to ever strike the U.S., claiming more than 8000 lives when the storm surge caught the residents of this island city by surprise.

Hurricane Katrina developed initially as a tropical depression (TD #12 of the season) in the southeastern Bahamas on August 23rd. This tropical depression strengthened into Tropical Storm Katrina the next day. It then moved slowly along a northwesterly then westerly track through the Bahamas, increasing in strength during this time. A few hours before landfall in south Florida at around 6.30 EDT on August 25th, Katrina strengthened to become a category 1 (windspeeds of 75mph or greater) hurricane. Landfall occurred between Hallandale Beach and North Miami Beach, Florida, with windspeeds of approximately 80 mph. Gusts of above 90 mph were measured as Katrina came ashore. As the storm moved southwest across the tip of the Florida peninsula, Katrina's winds decreased slightly before regaining hurricane strength in the Gulf of Mexico. Given that Katrina spent only seven hours over land, its strength was not significantly diminished and it quickly re-intensified shortly after moving over the warm waters of the Gulf.

Katrina moved almost due westward after entering the Gulf of Mexico. A mid-level ridge centered over Texas weakened and moved westward allowing Katrina to gradually turn to the northwest and then north into the weakness in the ridging over the days that followed. Atmospheric and sea-surface conditions (an upper level anticyclone over the Gulf and warm SSTs) were conducive to cyclone's rapid intensification, which lead to Katrina attaining 'major hurricane' status on the afternoon of the 26th.

Continuing to strengthen and move northwards during the next 48 hours, Katrina reached maximum windspeeds on the morning of Sunday August 28th of 150 kts (category 5), and its minimum central pressure dropped that afternoon to 902 mb - the 4th lowest on record for an Atlantic storm. Although Katrina, at its peak strength was comparable to Camille's intensity, it was a significantly larger storm and impacted a broader area of the Gulf coast. Although tropical cyclones of category 5 strength are rarely sustained for long durations (due to internal dynamics), Katrina remained a strong category 4 strength hurricane despite the entrainment of dryer air and an opening of the eyewall to the south and southwest before landfall on the morning of the 29th. Landfalling windspeeds at Grand Isle, LA were approximately 140 mph with a central pressure of 920mb - the 3rd lowest on record for a landfalling Atlantic storm in the US.

Below is a synopsis of the conditions that produced historic Hurricane Katrina, as well as some information of rain and wind records and a very preliminary description of the major impacts.

Rain, Wind, Storm Surge

Eastern Florida: During its initial landfall in southern Florida, Katrina generated over 5 inches of rainfall across a large area of southeastern Florida. An analysis by NOAA's Climate Prediction Center shows that parts of the region received heavy rainfall, over 15 inches in some locations, which caused localized flooding. Winds at landfall north of Miami were 80 mph (category 1 strength), leading to some damage and extensive power outages.

Gulf Coast: Rainfall from Katrina's outer bands began affecting the Gulf coast well before landfall. As Katrina came ashore on August 29th, rainfall exceeded rates of 1 inch/hour across a large area of the coast. NOAA's Climate

Reference Network Station in Newton, MS (60 miles east of Jackson, MS) measured rainfall rates of over an inch an hour for 3 consecutive hours, with rates of over 0.5 in/hr for 5 hours during August 29th. Precipitation analysis from NOAA's Climate Prediction Center show that rainfall accumulations exceeded 8-10 inches along much of the hurricane's path and to the east of the track. Windspeeds over 140 mph were recorded at landfall in southeastern Louisiana while winds gusted to over 100 mph in New Orleans, just west of the eye. As the hurricane made its second landfall on the Mississippi/Louisiana border, windspeeds were approximately 110 kts (125 mph). Gusts of over 80mph were recorded in Mobile and 90 mph in Biloxi, MS. The central pressure at landfall was 920 mb, which ranked 3rd lowest on record for US-landfalling storms behind Camille (909 mb) and the Labor Day hurricane that struck the Florida Keys in 1935 (892 mb). Hurricane Andrew in 1992 dropped to fourth, as its central pressure was 922 mb at landfall. Katrina also reached a minimum central pressure of 902 mb at its peak, ranking 4th lowest on record for all Atlantic basin hurricanes.

Inland: As the storm moved inland and weakened to a tropical storm on the 29th, rainfall became the primary impact. Rainfall amounts exceeded 2-4 inches across a large area from the Gulf coast to the Ohio Valley. As a result, flood watches and warnings were common across these regions. Rain bands from Katrina also produced tornadoes causing further damage in areas such as Georgia.

IMPACTS

LOSS OF LIFE: From the Gulf states (principally Louisiana and Mississippi), the loss of life is unknown but will likely reach well into the hundreds and possibly higher. It is clearly one of the most devastating natural disasters in recent US history. From Katrina's first landfall in Florida, while it was at category one strength, initial estimates suggest 11 deaths resulted.

FLOODING: The loss of life and property damage was worsened by breaks in the levees that separate New Orleans from surrounding lakes. At least 80% of New Orleans was under flood water on August 31st, largely as a result of levee failures from Lake Pontchartrain. The combination of strong winds, heavy rainfall and storm surge led to breaks in the earthen levee after the storm passed, leaving some parts of New Orleans under 20 feet of water. Storm surge from Mobile Bay led to inundation of Mobile, Alabama causing imposition of a dusk-to-dawn curfew for the City. Large portions of Biloxi and Gulfport, Mississippi were underwater as a result of a 20 to 30+ foot storm surge which flooded the cities.

OIL INDUSTRY: A major economic impact for the nation was the disruption to the oil industry from Katrina. Preliminary estimates from the Mineral Management Service suggest that oil production in the Gulf of Mexico was reduced by 1.4 million barrels per day (or 95 % of the daily Gulf of Mexico production) as a result of the hurricane. Gasoline had reached a record high price/gallon as of Monday August 30th with concerns over refinery capacity apparently driving the increase. More information is available from a Department of Energy report.

POWER OUTAGES: Over 1.7 million people lost power as a result of the storm in the Gulf states, with power companies estimating that it will take more than several weeks to restore power to some locations. Drinking water was also unavailable in New Orleans due to a broken water main that serves the city. Power was lost to 1.3 million customers in southeastern Florida from the initial landfall on August 24th.

COST: Estimates for insured damages for Hurricane Katrina are still extremely preliminary and properly assessing losses will take weeks or months. However, the cost of Katrina will certainly be a minimum of several billion dollars and might exceed losses from Hurricane Andrew. Andrew caused $15.5 billion in insured damage in 1992. Adjusted for inflation, Andrew resulted in more than $25 billion in insured damage.

TRAVEL: Both of New Orleans' airports were flooded and closed on August 30th and bridges of Interstate 10 leading east out of the city were destroyed. Most of the coastal highways along the Gulf were impassable in places and most minor roads near the shore were still underwater or covered in debris as of August 30th. Katrina also disrupted travel as it headed inland, with more than 2 inches of rain falling across a large area from the coast to parts of Ohio during the 48 hours after Katrina made landfall.

Flooding takes place after Hurricane Katrina hit New Orleans, Monday Morning, Aug. 29, 2005. Following the storm Louisiana officials said people in some swamped neighborhood were feared dead, but gave no immediate numbers. (AP Photo/Eric Gay)

Hurricane winds shred an American flag in downtown New Orleans, Louisiana as Hurricane Katrina passes over the Crescent City on Monday, Aug. 29, 2005. (AP Photo/Bill Haber)

EVACUATION

New Orleans residents are evacuated by boat after flood water continues to rise on Wednesday, Aug. 31, 2005. Thousands of residents who rode out Hurricane Katrina are now seeking a way out of the besieged city. (AP Photo/Bill Haber)

Residents are rescued by helicopter from the floodwaters of Hurricane Katrina Thursday, Sept. 1, 2005 in New Orleans. (AP Photo/David J. Phillip)

Residents wait on a rooftop to be rescued from the floodwaters of Hurricane Katrina Thursday, Sept. 1, 2005 in New Orleans. (AP Photo/David J. Phillip, Pool)

Orleans Parish prisoners are evacuated from the floodwaters of Hurricane Katrina Wednesday, Aug. 31, 2005 in New Orleans. (AP Photo/David J. Phillip)

Some of the thousands of Hurricane Katrina victims are evacuated to buses from the Convention Center in New Orleans, La., Saturday, Sept. 3, 2005. After days of waiting, hunderds of people were evacuated from the city by bus and helicopter. (AP Photo/Eric Gay)

Deaths by State

Alabama	2
Florida	14
Georgia	2
Kentucky	1
Louisiana	1,577*
Mississippi	238
Ohio	2
TOTAL	**1,836**
Add'l missing	705

•Includes out-of-state evacuees
counted by Lousiana

Hurricane Katrina refugees receive donations of clothes at Texas College in Tyler, Texas on Wednesday, Sept. 14, 2005. (AP Photo/Tyler Morning Telegraph, Tom Worner)

The floor of Houston's Astrodome is covered with cots and evacuees from Hurricane Katrina Sept. 4, 2005, in Texas. (AP Photo/Mandatory Credit:Christopher Morris/VII)

A man waves to greeters as he walks with a young girl upon their arrival in San Diego with a group of approximately 80 refugees from Hurricane Katrina Sunday, Sept. 4, 2005. A private citzen donated an airplane that transported 80 people consisting of approximately 15 families. (AP Photo/Lenny Ignelzi)

Dr Louis Cataldie, medical examiner for the state of Louisiana, stands outside the morgue set up to house Katrina victims Friday, Feb. 10,2006, St. Gabriel, LA. Officially, 1,079 people died in Louisiana following Hurricane Katrina but family members of about 300 missing people have called the state looking for loved ones.. Dr. Cataldie fears some may also be under debris in crushed houses. Final Katrina death count likely to climb but unclear how high. (AP Photo/Mary Ann Chastain)

Former Presidents Bill Clinton, left, and George H.W. Bush, right, are seen together during a news conference at the University of New Orleans, Wednesday, Dec. 7, 2005 in New Orleans. Bush and Clinton, who have raised at least $100 million for Hurricane Katrina victims, announced $90 million worth of grants Wednesday, including $30 million for higher education institutions along the Gulf Coast. (AP Photo/Chitose Suzuki)

Chicago Cubs pitcher Jerome Williams, right, collects donations for victims of Hurricane Katrina outside Wrigley Field before the start of the Chicago Cubs game with the St. Louis Cardinals, Thursday, Sept. 15, 2005, in Chicago. (AP Photo/Jeff Roberson)

Christian Mauroner, of New Orleans, motions to people dropping off clothing donations for Hurricane Katrina victims at a parking lot across the street from the Astrodome, Thursday, Sept. 1, 2005, in Houston. Mauroner evacuated from New Orleans over the weekend to stay with relatives in Houston but felt a need to help the less fortunate evacuees. The parking lot drop site sprang up after people were turned away from donating at the Astrodome shelter. (AP Photo/Pat Sullivan)

Survivors of Hurricane Katrina who are staying at the Astrodome head to money machines put up in front of the Reliant Center in Houston on Friday, Sept. 9, 2005, to get their first cash since being routed from their homes last week in New Orleans. Money machines sprouted up around the Reliant Center to accomodate the survivors who received debit cards from both the American Red Cross and FEMA on Friday. (AP Photo/David Zalubowski)

FEMA RESPONSE

FEMA has provided nearly $6 billion directly to Hurricane Katrina victims for housing and other needs assistance through the Individuals and Households Assistance Program. This is the most money every provided by FEMA for and single natural disaster.

Individual Assistance

Housing and Other Needs
LA - $4.76 billion
MS - $1.249 billion
AL - $128 million

Public Assistance

Protective Measures, Debris Removal, Roads & Bridges, Public Buildings

LA - $3.Billion
MS - $1.2 Billion
AL - $61 Million

Former Federal Emergency Management Agency (FEMA) Director Michael Brown defends his response to Hurricane Katrina on Capitol Hill Tuesday, Sept. 27, 2005, during testimony before a House select committee investigating preparation and response to the hurricane. (AP Photo/Dennis Cook)

Kim Newton walks with her dogs Boots and Rocket in front of her FEMA trailer which is decorated for Christmas in front of her home that was heavily damaged by Hurricane Katrina in the St. Bernard Parish town of Chalmette, La. just outside New Orleans, Friday, Dec. 23, 2005. (AP Photo/Gerald Herbert)

This aerial photo showing one of many FEMA trailer parks around the region, was taken in August, 2006. The trailers offer assistance to the thousands of families displaced by Hurricane Katrina. (Buddy Moffey, ©CKI, Inc.)

RED CROSS

Red Cross estimates that Hurricane Katrina relief efforts will exceed $2 billion. This includes meeting the urgent needs of the survivors, food and shelter, financial assistance and physical and mental health services.

Red Cross financial assistance will have been distributed to 1.2 families (more than 3.7 million hurricane survivors).

The Red Cross has provided survivors with nearly 3.42 million overnight stays in 1,100 shelters across 27 states and the District of Columbia.

More than 219,500 Red Cross disaster relief workers from all 50 states, Puerto Rico and Virgin Islands have responded to the needs of the survivors.

27.4 million hot meals and 25.2 million snacks have been served to the hurricane survivors to date.

The Red Cross has received approximately $2.7 billion in gifts and pledges to date for the relief efforts.

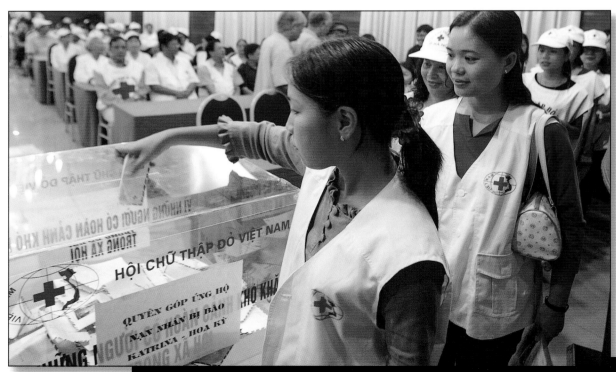

Vietnamese Red Cross workers donate money for victims of Hurricane Katrina at the Army hotel in Hanoi on Friday September 9, 2005. The Vietnamese Red Cross has donated US$20,000 and is continuing calling for more. The Vietnamese Red Cross has offered the U.S. governement to send a team of 15 doctors to help survivors of Hurricane Katrina. (AP Photo/Tran Quang Tuan)

Homes destroyed by floodwaters from Hurricane Katrina are shown in this aerial view Tuesday, Aug. 30, 2005 in New Orleans. Hurricane Katrina did extensive damage when it made landfall on Monday. (AP Photo/David J. Phillip)

Trucks enter the Old Gentilly Landfill in New Orleans, Tuesday, Nov. 8, 2005. State environmental regulators on Tuesday defended the use of the old landfill for Hurricane Katrina debris, rejecting contentions by environmentalists that the site might be a Superfund in the making. (AP Photo/Tony Dejak)

Containers sit among debris from Hurricane Katrina Wednesday, Aug. 31, 2005, in Gulfport, Miss. (AP Photo/David J. Phillip)

A sea of refrigerators, full of rotting food, await cleaning and disposal at a landfill in New Orleans, Wednesday, Oct. 19, 2005. Authorities say the iceboxes pose health and environmental risks and symbolize a monumental task-digging New Orleans and other parts of southeastern Louisiana out from the mountain of debris created by Hurricanes Katrina and Rita. (AP Photo/Don Ryan).

Debris from Hurricane Katrina litters the road along casino row in Biloxi, Miss., Tuesday, Aug. 30, 2005. The storm caused major damage to the soon-to-open Hard Rock Casino and other gambling resorts on the Mississippi coast. (AP Photo/Jay Reevves)

BLUE ROOFS

A sign of damage after a hurricane is always the blue roofs. The blue roofs are actually blue tarps and can be seen all over the damaged areas. Some of these photos were taken a year after the storm hit the gulf region. The blue tarps were also a part of Mardi-Gras in February 2006.

AP Photo/Bill Haber?

Photo: Buddy Moffet, ©CKI, Inc.

(AP Photo/Mandatory Credit:Christopher Morris/VII)

Photo: Buddy Moffet, ©CKI, Inc.

DOWNTOWN N.O.

A view of New Orleans La., in the aftermath of Hurricane Katrina Sept. 5, 2005. New Orleans was badly hit by the hurricane which hit the U.S. Gulf Coast on Aug. 29, causing huge damage and triggering flooding across a wide area. (AP Photo/Mandatory Credit: Christopher Morris/VII)

Debris from a fallen building covers several buildings in downtown New Orleans after Hurricane Katrina battered the Louisiana Coast on Monday, Aug. 29, 2005. (AP Photo/Dave Martin)

Cars sit idle on flooded streets in downtown New Orleans after Hurricane Katrina came ashore on Monday, Aug. 29, 2005. (AP Photo/Dave Martin)

A view of New Orleans La., in the aftermath of Hurricane Katrina Sept. 8, 2005. New Orleans was badly hit by the hurricane which hit the U.S. Gulf Coast on Aug. 29, causing huge damage and triggering flooding across a wide area. (AP Photo/Mandatory Credit:Christopher Morris/VII)

Homes flooded by floodwaters from Hurricane Katrina sit near downtown New Orleans, Wednesday, Aug. 31, 2005 in Louisiana. (AP Photo/David J. Phillip)

A fire burns in warehouses along the river front, Saturday, Sept; 3, 2005, in New Orleans, LA.(AP Photo/Phil Coale)

Many of the warehouses along the river front were destroyed by Hurricane Katrina and the fires that broke out after. Photo taken July, 2006. (Buddy Moffet, ©CKI, Inc.)

This photo provided by the US Navy Thursday Sept. 1, 2005 shows an aerial view from a U.S. Navy helicopter from the USS Bataan (LHD5) showing the rising flood waters threatening the entire downtown New Orleans city center, including the famed New Orleans Saints SuperDome. Tens of thousands of displaced citizens sought shelter at the dome, before, during and after Hurricane Katrina, but have been forced to evacuate as flood waters continue to rise throughout the area. (AP Photo/US Navy - photographer's Mate Airman Jeremy L. Grisham)

This downtown aerial photo, July, 2006, shows the SuperDome which is still undergoing repairs to it's cover. (Buddy Moffet, ©CKI, Inc.)

Thousands of revelers jam Bourbon Street in the French Quarter during Mardi Gras in New Orleans Tuesday, Feb. 28, 2006. Much of the city is still uninhabitable six months after Hurricane Katrina devastated the area. (AP Photo/Bill Haber)

Carlie Kahn who decided not to evacuate is seen standing in his front yard Monday, Sept. 5, 2005, in Old Metairie, La. Residents of Jefferson Parish who fled from Hurricane Katrina were allowed to return home Monday for the first time since the storm. (AP Photo/Rick Bowmer)

Water is pumped out of a flooded Metairie, La., subdivision through a 30 inch pipe that pumps out 27,000 gallons of water per minute Tuesday Sept. 6, 2005. Water is now being pumped out of the city after officials repaired a broken flood wall. (AP Photo/Steven Senne)

Jon Andersen and Julienne Van Vliet use poles to push their boat along a street after returning home Monday, Sept. 5, 2005, in Old Metairie, La. Residents of Jefferson Parish who fled from Hurricane Katrina were allowed to return home Monday for the first time since the storm. (AP Photo/Rick Bowmer)

New Orleans Saints first round draft pick Reggie Bush is swarmed for his autograph by children from Franco's Athletic Club Summer Camp after the New Orleans Saints football mini camp practice in Metairie, Louisiana on Friday June2 , 2006. (AP Photo/Alex Brandon)

North Illinois Police Alarm System (ILEAS) SWAT team members patrol the devastated Lakeview district near the 17th Street Canal levee break while Urban Search and Rescue teams search the area, Thursday, Sept. 22, 2005, in New Orleans. (AP Photo/Kevork Djansezian)

A home devastated by Hurricane Katrina in the Lakeview area of New Orleans, is seen Wednesday, Feb. 22, 2006.(AP Photo/Carolyn Kaster)

Jeff Gottbreht, from Lincoln, Neb., Urban Search and Rescue task force, searches for survivors inside a flood damaged house near the 17th Street Canal levee break in the Lakeview district of New Orleans Thursday, Sept. 22, 2005. In the aftermath of Hurricane Katrina, New Orleans is keeping an eye on Hurricane Rita. (AP Photo/Kevork Djansezian)

This close up photo, taken in Lake View in July, 2006, shows the heavy machinery and equipment that is necessary to repair the damaged levee systems and flood control channels after Hurricane Katrina. Even after a year there is still major work to be done. (Buddy Moffet, ©CKI, Inc.)

Even after a year has passed after Katrina, there is continuous work being done to repair and strengthen the levees and flood control systems. This aerial photo shows the repairs that are taking place. (Buddy Moffet, ©CKI, Inc.)

Looking down over the West End Harbor area in Lake View, in July, 2006, it is hard to imagine that it is a year after Katrina. Boats still lay on roadways and boathouses remain damaged. (Buddy Moffet, ©CKI, Inc)

This tree, uprooted during Hurricane Katrina, still sits one year later on the side of the street near the 17th St. Canal. (Buddy Moffet, ©CKI, Inc)

The West End Harbor in Lake View took on a large amount of damage from Hurricane Katrina. This aerial view taken in August, 2006 still shows the devastation that took place. Notice the West End Lighthouse that was completely torn apart. (Buddy Moffet, ©CKI, Inc)

Several companies are raising money to help rebuild the West End Lighthouse that was destroyed during Hurricane Katrina. (Buddy Moffet, ©CKI, Inc.)

Taken in August, 2006, this photos shows thetemporary repairs that have been made to the 17th St. Canal. The breach in the levee during Hurricane Katrina caused major damage to the areas north of downtown. (Buddy Moffet, ©CKI, Inc.)

9th WARD

Floodwaters from Hurricane Katrina flow over a levee along Inner Harbor Navigaional Canal near downtown New Orleans Tuesday, Aug. 30, 2005. Hurricane Katrina did extensive damage when it made landfall on Monday. (AP Photo/David J. Phillip)

Members of the Louisiana Recovery Authority tours the New Orlean's hurricane-ravaged Lower 9th Ward, Wednesday, Oct. 26, 2005. Much of the 9th Ward was destroyed when the levee broke at the Industrial Canal during Hurricanes Katrina and Rita. (AP Photo/Robert F. Bukaty)

Beverly Evans covers her eyes as she rides through her neighborhood in the Lower 9th Ward for the first time since its was destroyed by Hurricane Katrina, Thursday, Oct. 27, 2005, in New Orleans. The city provided 9th Ward residents with the opportunity to take bus tours for a brief look at their community. (AP Photo/Robert F. Bukat

A Chinook helicopter drops sandbags to repair the breach in the Industrial Canal levee, Sunday, Sept. 25, 2005, in New Orleans. The storm surge created by Hurricane Rita eroded repairs made after Katrina and sent water surging back into the already devastated Ninth Ward. (AP Photo/Kevork Djansezian)

Britain's Prince Charles, front 2nd left, and his wife Camilla, Duchess of Cornwall, front 2nd right, talk with US Coast Guard Vice Adm. Thad Allen, right, and Cpt. Thomas Atkin as the Royal couple walk through the heavily damaged Ninth Ward towards the repaired Industrial Canal Levee in New Orleans, La on Friday, Nov. 4, 2005. The Royal couple are visiting New Orleans in a show of support for the gulf coast region that has been ravaged by Hurricanes Katrina and Rita during their eight day tour of the United States (AP Photo/Lucas Jackson, Pool)

The 9th Ward was completely devastated by the Hurricane. Most of the homes will have to be built from the ground up. Notice the levee that is nearly finished being rebuilt. Photo taken August, 2006. (Buddy Moffet, ©CKI, Inc.)

Homes in the 9th Ward that were destroyed during Katrina are only now being bulldozed a year later. Most of these houses will have to be rebuilt. (Buddy Moffet, ©CKI, Inc.)

Thousands of homes were damaged or destoyed during Hurricane Katrina. The 9th Ward was hard hit and a still shows the scars a year later. Thos photo, taken in August, 2006 also shows the levee system that is being rebuilt. (Buddy Moffet, ©CKI, Inc)

One of the many organizations offering tools, clothes and supplies. This is the Common Ground Distribution Center located in the 9th Ward, New Orleans. (Buddy Moffet, ©CKI, Inc.)

This area just north of the 9th Ward in New Orleans is a recycling center where debris from around the surrounding neighborhoods is brought in an sorted before being shipped out. (Buddy Moffet, ©CKI, Inc.)

A military helicopter flies over flooded homes in Chalmette, La., Tuesday, Sept. 6 2005. Flood water remains high in Chalmette, more than a week after Hurricane Katrina devastated the area. (AP Photo/Steven Senne)

As floodwaters from Hurricane Katrina receed, a layer of mud covers the streets and home,s Thursday, Sept. 8, 2005 in St. Bernard Parish near New Orleans. (AP Photo/David J. Phillip, pool)

Remnants of homes destroyed by Hurricane Katrina are seen in Sheel Beach of St. Bernard Parish, La. Sat. Dec. 17, 2005. (AP Photo/Gerald Herbert)

A fishing boat is still in the middle of the street in St. Bernard Parish La. Thursday Feb. 23, 2006. Six months afer Hurricane Katrina, the region is still struggling with the devastation. (AP Photo/Alex Brandon)

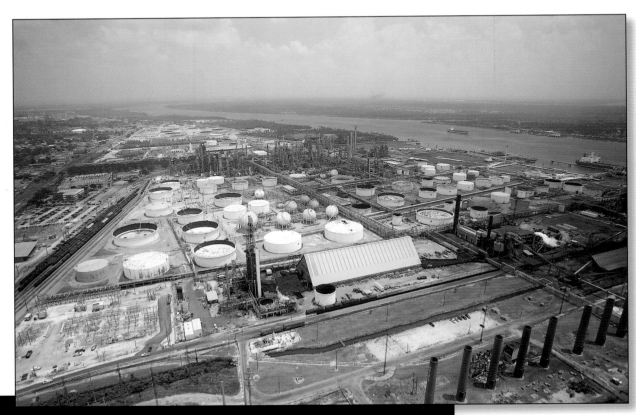

Thousands of companies were affected by Hurricane Katrina especially large oil refineries like this one. There are many FEMA trailers set up around the facility, probably for many of the workers and their families. (Buddy Moffet, ©CKI, Inc.)

Construction crews from the organization Habitat For Humanity are well under way buidling new homes for the many families displaced after Hurricane Katrina. (Buddy Moffet,©CKI, Inc.)

An aerial view of St. Bernard Parish taken in July, 2006. Reggie Bush, recently drafted by the New Orleans Saints Football team, donated money to have the football field in the center of the picture resurfaced. (Buddy Moffet, ©CKI, Inc.)

TWIN SPAN BRIDGES

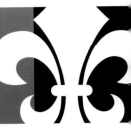

A Louisiana state trooper leads the first commuters across one span of the twin spans in New Orleans, Friday Oct. 14, 2005. The Interstate 10 bridges were damaged by Hurricane Katrina. (AP Photo/Bill Haber)

The broken I-10 bridge between New Orleans and Slidell is shown in this aerial Sunday, Sept. 11, 2005. (AP Photo/David J. Phillip)

This photo taken in August, 2006 of the Interstate-10 bridge that connects New Orleans and Slidell shows the repairs that have been made to the bridge. (Buddy Moffet, ©CKI, Inc.)

Homes and cars submerged underwater are shown in Slidell, La., Tuesday Aug. 30, 2005, after Hurricane Katrina swept through the region. (AP Photo/Mari Darr Welch)

Boats and heavily damaged homes are seen in the aftermath of Hurricane Katrina in Slidell, La., Sept. 16, 2005. Katrina hit the region on August 29 causing numerous deaths and severe property damage. (AP Photo/Mandatory Credit:Christopher Morris/VII)

An U.S. flag flies Saturday, Jan. 14, 2006, over a residence demolished by Hurricane Katrina, on Highway 11 in Slidell, La. (AP Photo/Ben Margot)

A boat sits on a house damaged by Hurricane Katrina Tuesday, Aug. 30, 2005 in Slidell, La. (AP Photo/David J. Phillip)

This photo, taken in August, 2006, shows a home on the north shore area of Slidell, LA that lies in ruins after Hurricane Katrina hit a year ago. (Buddy Moffet, ©CKI, Inc.)

Debris from destroyed homes still sits a year later near Oak Harbor Golf Club, Slidell, LA. (Buddy Moffet, ©CKI, Inc.)

Debris and trash sit on the lawn of a resident in the Slidell, LA area. Many of the homes cannot be inhabited so trailers from FEMA are used as temporary homes. (Buddy Moffet, ©CKI, Inc.)

Pam Koll negotiates her way through fallen trees and a mud covered road to get to what remains of her home in Bay St. Louis, Miss., on Friday, Sept. 2, 2005. Koll's house, built 15-feet high on stilts, was inundated with water from Hurricane Katrina. (AP Photo/Denis Paquin)

Highway 90 which crosses St. Louis Bay was completely destroyed by Hurricane Katrina. Crews are in the process of building a new bridge seen in this photo taken in July, 2006. (Buddy Moffet, ©CKI, Inc.)

As seen from this photo taken in July, 2006, the area along Beach Blvd. both structures and foliage were obliterated by Hurricane Katrina. (Buddy Moffet, ©CKI, Inc)

A photo of what once was a grand home, replaced now by a FEMA trailer, stands along Highway 90 in Pass Christian, Miss. on Friday April 14, 2006. (AP Photo/Alex Brandon)

A house sits on railroad tracks in Pass Christian, Miss., Tuesday, Nov. 29, 2005. Three months after Hurricane Katrina hit the Gulf Coast, the house remains where it came to rest during the storm. (AP Photo/Orlin Wagner)

A boat rests on top of the remains of a home in Pass Christian, Miss., Tuesday, Nov. 29, 2005. Three months after Hurricane Katrina many residents have yet to work on their damaged property. (AP Photo/Orlin Wagner)

GULF PORT, MS

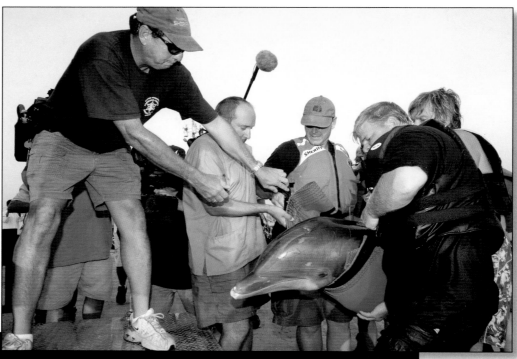

NOAA personnel as well as Gulfport Marine Oceanarium staff carry the Oceanarium's dolphin, Jill, to a transport truck in Gulfport Miss., Tuesday Sept 20, 2005 The dolphins were washed out of the Oceanarium's tank during hurricane Katrina. NOAA staff along with the Oceanarium's staff recovered all the remaining dolphins. (AP Photo/Steve Helber)

An aerial view of the Gulfport Marine Oceanarium in Gulfport, MS. The Oceanrium was completely destroyed and there are plans to have a new facility built. Photo taken July, 2006. (Buddy Moffet, ©CKI, Inc.)

Workers demolish the Grand Casino, piece by piece, along Highway 90 in Gulfport, Miss. on Thursday May 4, 2006. (AP Photo/Alex Brandon)

Photo of the First Baptist Church, Gulfport, MS taken in July, 2006. (Buddy Moffet, ©CKI, Inc.)

A bridge on Highway 90 is shown Tuesday, Aug. 30, 2005 after it was hit by Hurricane Katrina Tuesday, Aug. 30, 2005 in Biloxi, Miss. (AP Photo/John Bazemore)

Vehicles pushed by the storm surge from Hurricane Katrina pile up in a Biloxi, Miss. neighboorhood, Tuesday, Aug. 30, 2005. (AP Photo/ John David Mercer, Pool)

Local kids search for a pair shoes in a donation area set up in a destroyed gas station in West Biloxi, Miss., on Monday, Sept. 5, 2005. Hurricane Katrina has left thousands of residents homeless and in need of clothes. (AP Photo/Denis Paquin)

A truck rests in the Back Bay of Biloxi near the destroyed Palace Casino, Friday, Sept. 9, 2005, in Biloxi, Miss., after Hurricane Katrina hit the area. (AP Photo/San Antonio Express-News, Edward A. Ornelas)

This aerial taken in July 2006 of downtown Biloxi shows the damage done to the hotels and casinos during Hurricane Katrina. The Hard Rock Hotel and Casino was scheduled to open the same week the hurricane hit the area. (Buddy Moffet, ©CKI, Inc.)

The Palace Casino in Biloxi, Miss. partially lies underwater Tuesday Aug. 30, 2005 after Hurricane Katrina passed through the area. (AP Photo/Peter Cosgrove)

This photo, taken in July, 2006, shows the area where the Palace Casino lay parially underwater after Hurricane Katrina moved through the area. (Buddy Moffet, ©CKI, Inc.)

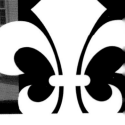

Louisiana Gov. Kathleen Blanco, right, is followed by Virginia Gov. Tim Kaine as they walks between the puddles at the Habitat for Humanity Musicians' Village in New Orleans on Saturday, July 15, 2006, as part of the Southern Governors' Association meeting this weekend. On Saturday, the association's member governors and volunteers helped with the construction of a new housing community in New Orleans' Upper Ninth Ward. The project, known as the Musicians' Village, was conceived by native jazz musicians Branford Marsalis and Harry Connick Jr. in partnership with New Orleans Area Habitat for Humanity. The community is just under way but plans for 300 houses as a way to help displaced musicians and others come home. (AP Photo/Alex Brandon)

Saxophone musician Daniel Oestreicher works at the Habitat for Humanity Musicians' Village in New Orleans on Saturday, July 15, 2006. Daniel lived in the mid-city area of New Orleans and his home was heavily damaged in the aftermath of Hurricane Katrina. He is working so that he can get one of the houses being built. The project, known as the Musicians' Village, was conceived by native jazz musicians Branford Marsalis and Harry Connick Jr. in partnership with New Orleans Area Habitat for Humanity. The community is just under way but plans for 300 houses as a way to help displaced musicians and others come home. (AP Photo/Alex Brandon)

Sen. Barack Obama, D-Ill., helps paint a home at the Habitat for Humanity project at the Musicians' Village, Friday July 21, 2006 in New Orleans. Obama spent the day touring parts of the city damaged by the aftermath of Hurricane Katrina. (AP Photo/Rob Carr)

Caliopie Georgiadis left, from Brooklyn, N.Y., and Lindsey Murray, from Livermore, Calif., work on a house that was heavily damaged by Hurricane Katrina in New Orleans on Thursday, Sept. 14, 2006. (AP Photo/Alex Brandon)

Cynthia Smith poses in the lobby of the Beau Rivage Casino and Resort in Biloxi, Miss., on the day of its re-opening Tuesday, Aug. 29, 2006. The Beau Rivage has been closed the past year, since Hurricane Katrina flooded its interior. An estimated 15,000 gaming industry employees on Mississippi's casino-dotted coast were without jobs immediately after the storm. With the reopening of eight casinos, nearly 13,000 are back at work. (AP Photo/Nicole LaCour Young)

The Norwegian Sun cruise ship enters the Port of New Orleans before dawn as the first cruise ship to homeport in New Orleans since Hurricane Katrina, Sun., Oct. 15, 2006. (AP Photo/Cheryl Gerber)